MW00879453

BESHLIE'S
COUNTRYSIDE

To Wendy Craig and Miriam Stoppard M.D. M.R.C.P.

Published in association with

The National Trust
36 Queen Anne's Gate, London SW1 9AS

First published in Great Britain in 1988 by
ORCHARD BOOKS
10 Golden Square, London W1R 3AF
Orchard Books Australia
14 Mars Road, Lane Cove NSW 2066
Orchard Books Canada
20 Torbay Road, Markham, Ontario 23P 1G6
Published in association with Gallery Five
121 King Street, Hammersmith, London W6 9JG
1 85213 042 3
Typeset in Great Britain by P4 Graphics
Printed in Great Britain by Purnell Book Production

BESHLIE'S COUNTRYSIDE

THE BOOK OF

The Coppice-Cutter, Trug-Maker & Besom-Maker

ORCHARD BOOKS

in association with The National Trust
London

Field Vole   Stinging Nettle
Scentless Mayweed   Woodland Brome
Woodland Meadow Grass   Yorkshire Fog
Meadow Foxtail

The Coppice-Cutter

A coppice is the name for a small wood of about three acres, and oak, hazel and chestnut are among the coppiced woods. These special trees were not allowed to mature, as wood from adult trees was of no use to the makers of hurdles or trugs, two of this woodman's customers.

The Coppice-cutter lived near the coppices he worked. He bought the pliant greenwood and harvested it. Quite often he found a rod suitable for a shepherd's crook, a thumbstick — a long stick with a forked

top you hook your thumb between — or a walking stick. This was cut with a *hatchet* or one-handed axe, and trimmed with a *billhook*, as he is doing in the main picture.

During long winter nights by the fire, the Coppice-cutter often carved the shapes of woodland animals or birds on the stick handles. There is one in the small picture. A shepherd's crook is often carved with a ewe or a sheep-dog or both. A fox and a hound often adorn the twin tops of a thumbstick.

Coppice wood was cut down almost to the rootstock, called *stools*. From these, new wood grew each year. A willow coppice, grown near water,

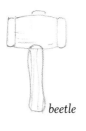

beetle

stools

10

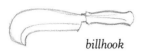

billhook

hatchet

felling-axe

would yield a dozen rods
to each stool.

While waiting for the new
wood to grow, which could
take three to four years, he worked
another two or three acres. If he bought
a neglected coppice, the Coppice-cutter
might have to fell large trees. For this
he had a heavy two-handed *felling-axe*.

Wood unsuitable for hurdles or palings
was sold to other craftsmen for thatching
spars and for besom-making and to villagers
for bean poles or kindling. You can see some
chestnut paling in the main picture. As with
most country occupations, very little was
wasted.

Field Mouse   Hairless Catmint
Creeping Jenny   Yellow Meadow Vetchling

The Trug-Maker

Trugs were once called boatbaskets, because the word trug is from the Anglo-Saxon 'trog', meaning boat. Trugs have a second similarity to boats in that the boards overlap. In boat-building this is called clinker-built.

Villagers used trugs for carrying produce of garden or field about the farm. Vegetables could be carried from garden to store, and from the store to the kitchen. They could also be used for taking small amounts of produce to market. Trugs were not shopping baskets, but handy, long-lasting and reliable garden baskets.

Contrary to most other baskets, the rim, handle and bracing pieces, all of chestnut or ash, are made first. The body is made of thin pollarded white willow, cut into exact patterns, then steamed and bent into a curved boat shape. Small to medium trugs have seven boards.

Sitting at his work table which holds his tools and nails, while holding the *frame*, the Trug-maker first nails the centre-board onto the frame at each end. He then nails in the piece called the second-board, using non-rust copper nails with flat heads.

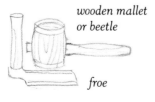

wooden mallet or beetle

froe

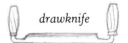

drawknife

The Trug-maker uses a *froe* and *wooden mallet* to split or cleave the willow strips. Then he sits on a shavehorse, which is to his left in the main picture. He can then put each board into the jaws of the horse. This allows him to use both hands, one on each handle of the *drawknife*, with which he smooths the board.

frame

Large or bushel trugs have no handle, as two arms are needed to carry such a heavy weight, so two openings are left for hands, one each side. Small blocks of wood which form feet and keep the basket off wet ground are fitted. These also strengthen the base.

Then the Trug-maker is ready for a nice cup of tea, brewed in the old-fashioned way by putting the tea in the kettle.

15

Wood Mouse   Corn Cockle
Feverfew   Ivy-leaved Toadflax
Rape or Cole

The Besom-Maker

Still the finest yard and garden brooms there are, besoms have been made since Saxon times. They are not pushed or pulled as are other brooms. Sweeping is achieved by a sideways movement.

They have been called witches' brooms since early days when one stood outside every cottage door. One can imagine an old woman, with a reputation for being a witch, using this handy stick to drive away jeering children.

Brushwood — the crowns or tops of birch

17

trees — is cut in winter, stacked, and left to season. This is an essential process. Brooms made from new crowns would disintegrate.

The craftsman begins to make the broom by selecting long twigs for the centre, and short bushy ones for the outside. Experience has taught him how to make a nicely shaped bundle. Sitting astride his broomhorse which is to his left in the main picture, and holding

18

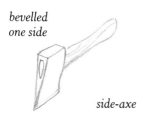

*bevelled
one side*

side-axe

the binding taut, he winds
it round the bundle in two places,
as far apart as the palm of his
hand. I have found the honeysuckle
vine to be excellent for binding.
The Besom-maker then chops all
the uneven butt-ends off the besom.

In what may seem a backwards-first operation after the broom head is made, the handle, called a tail, is sharpened to a point and pushed into the head. The besom is then turned upside-down and the end of the tail banged on a wooden block. The handle goes all the way in, then a *nail* is put from the binding into the tail. It is worth remembering that this is the correct way of getting any tool handle back on. Never hit a *hammer* head on the ground, always the handle.

peg

bit

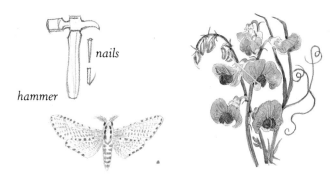

hammer

nails

Broken or cut off twigs were sold to fire the Baker's oven, or the little clome bread-ovens built into the side of cottage fireplaces. These have beautiful domed brick ceilings.

Once the twigs had heated the bricks, the ash was raked out, in went the loaves, and the iron door was closed. Very early clome ovens had thin tin doors. Cast-iron doors had hinges, tin ones were free-standing.

21